FOCUS ON THE FAMILY'S

The Truth project ®

Study Guide

For more study aids and other resources, visit **mytruthproject.org**

Editor: Ray Seldomridge
Design: Mike Harrigan

ISBN: 978-1-58997-730-3

Contents

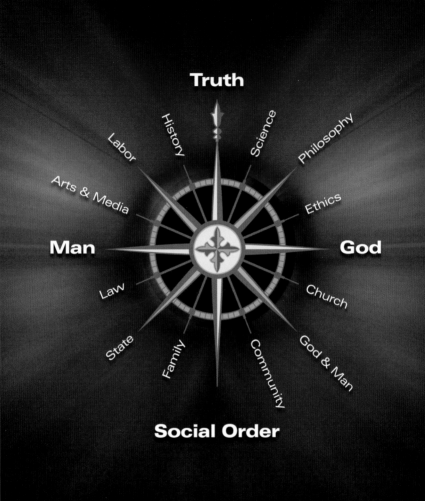

Truth

History   Science

Labor   Philosophy

Arts & Media   Ethics

Man   God

Law   Church

State   God & Man

Family   Community

Social Order

Preface

This series is designed to take you on a guided worldview tour, following the points of the "worldview compass." The compass will direct your thinking on four fundamental issues: truth, God, man, and the social order. Along the way, you will learn how to organize and evaluate various opposing ideas that all claim to be the truth. But our ultimate goal is not simply to gain knowledge. It is to "look upon the face of God"—and to be transformed in the process.

FOCUS ON THE FAMILY'S

The Truth Project

Study Guide

An In-Depth Christian Worldview Experience

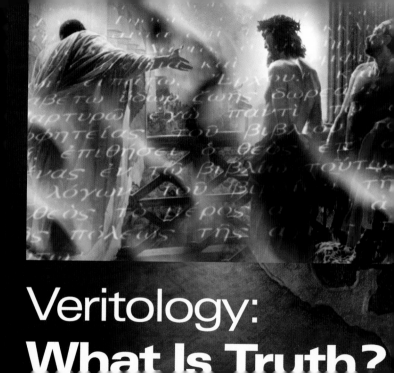

Veritology:
What Is Truth?

Introduction

What is truth? Why is it important? What role does it play in the biblical view of the world, God's purpose for the cosmos, His will for mankind, His plan of salvation, and the way we live our personal lives?

In this first tour, Dr. Del Tackett explains why every man and woman has to choose between God's truth claims and the opposing perspective of the world, the flesh, and the devil.

TheTruthProject

Quote Unquote

What did they say? Fill in the blanks as you watch this presentation.

1. There is a very close link between the issue of salvation and the issue of _____. —*Del Tackett*

2. Every sin that besets us can be traced back fundamentally to the belief in a _____. —*Del Tackett*

3. When we look at those who stand opposed to God's truth, we view them as _____. —*Del Tackett*

4. The single most important question any human being can ask is …
"_____ _____ _____?" —*Ravi Zacharias*

5. Truth is defined as that which corresponds to _____ as perceived by God.—*R.C. Sproul*

6. He feeds on ashes, a deluded heart misleads him; he cannot save himself, or say, "Is not this thing in my right hand a _____?"
—*Isaiah 44:20*

7. We trade in the majesty of God to worship a _____ _____ or a totem pole or a lizard. —*R.C. Sproul*

8. Our actions reflect what we believe to be _____ _____. —*Del Tackett*

9. Truth is fundamentally about _____ _____ _____.—*Os Guinness*

10. Behind every truth claim of God is the very _____ and _____ and _____ of God. —*Del Tackett*

Notes or Questions

While watching the video, use these lines to record your thoughts, any facts you want to remember, questions that arise, etc.

_____

_____

_____

_____

_____

_____

_____

_____

_____

_____

_____

_____

_____

_____

_____

_____

_____

_____

_____

_____

_____

_____

_____

_____

_____

_____

"For this reason I was born, and for this I came into the world."

John 18:37

Truth 1 | Why Jesus Came

Jesus said that He had entered the world "to testify to the truth" (John 18:37).

1. What did Jesus mean by this? Why is it important?

_____

_____

_____

_____

2. How does Jesus' statement relate to other aspects of His mission? What does truth have to do with *your* salvation?

_____

_____

_____

_____

_____

Truth 2 | World at War

A cosmic battle rages between the truth claims of God and the illusions of the world, the flesh, and the devil.

1. Identify some of the illusions about life that our culture tries to pass off as truth. What, for example, does the world say about the nature of man, or about our purpose for existence? How does our society say we can find happiness?

_____

_____

_____

_____

2. What happens when our fallen inner nature leads us to ignore a truth claim of God and instead believe in a lie? Pinpoint some illusions that have been the most deceptive or harmful in your own life.

_____

_____

_____

3. How do you feel about living in the midst of a war? Do you see yourself as a soldier? Why or why not?

_____

_____

_____

4. How should we relate to people who do not know the truth in Jesus Christ? If they are not our enemies, what are they?

_____

_____

_____

Truth 3 | Truth = What Is

Truth is that which conforms to fact or reality.

1. What do people mean when they refer to "my truth" or "your truth"? How should we respond to them?

_____

_____

_____

2. What is insanity? Have you ever been "insane"? Explain. In what sense is this world becoming more insane?

_____

_____

_____

3. Do you *really* believe that what you believe is really real? What assumption lies behind this question? What is the clearest indicator of your core beliefs?

_____

_____

_____

4. What does *faith* mean? Explain the difference between "faith in faith" and faith in the truth claims of God.

_____

_____

_____

Wrap-Up

In almost every area of life, the perspective of contemporary culture stands in direct opposition to the worldview presented in the Bible. Hence our culture is not only filled with lies but is heading in the direction of social insanity.

The question that Pilate asked—"What is truth?"—is the most important issue facing our society today. Every one of us must examine our response to this challenge: "Do you *really* believe that what you believe is really real?"

the first column to its definition in the second column. Terms are found in the lecture or at mytruthproject.org.

1. antithesis

    a. battle between God's truth and the lies of the world

2. veritology

    b. false source of salvation, sustenance, or power

3. cosmic battle

    c. comprehensive set of truth claims

4. pathology

    d. losing touch with reality; believing a lie is real

5. idol

    e. complete or exact opposite of something

6. Jewels in the Cave

    f. specific topics or truth claims of particular interest

7. pernicious lie

    g. departure or deviation from

Check It Out

For your reference and further review, here are some of the key Scripture passages that were mentioned in the video you just watched.

Isaiah 44:17-20

John 4:24; 8:32; 14:6,16-17; 16:13; 17:17; 18:33-38

Romans 1:18,25

Ephesians 6:14

2 Thessalonians 2:9-13

1 Timothy 2:3-4

2 Timothy 2:24-26; 4:3-4

1 John 4:6

Philosophy & Ethics

Introduction

According to contemporary culture, what you see is what you get. Nothing exists beyond the material universe. So the world is a closed box—a cosmic cube that embraces all of reality.

But when God is excluded, philosophy loses its universal reference point and cannot discover true reality. And without God, it makes no sense to talk about right and wrong.

TheTruthProject

Quote Unquote

What did they say? Fill in the blanks as you watch this presentation.

1. See to it that no one takes you _____through hollow and deceptive philosophy, which depends upon human tradition. —*Colossians 2:8*

2. The _____ is all that is, or ever was, or ever will be. —*Carl Sagan*

3. We are bombarded by _____ _____ from everywhere.
   —*Del Tackett*

4. Philosophy is a scientific quest to discover _____ _____.
   —*R.C. Sproul*

5. God has given us the _____ so that we might understand the _____. —*Del Tackett*

6. When I die, I am absolutely certain that I'm going to be completely
   _____. —*William Provine*

7. Morality looks at the verb "is".... Ethics looks at the word
   "_____." —*R.C. Sproul*

8. Only ____ percent of born-again believers in America have a biblical
   worldview. —*Del Tackett*

9. The church's singular failure in recent decades has been the failure
   to see Christianity as a _____ _____ ... that governs
   every area of existence. —*Charles Colson*

10. We are called as Christian people not to be conformed to this world
    but to be _____. —*Del Tackett*

Notes or Questions

While watching the video, use these lines to record your thoughts, any facts you want to remember, questions that arise, etc.

_____

_____

_____

_____

_____

_____

_____

_____

_____

_____

_____

_____

_____

_____

_____

_____

_____

_____

_____

_____

_____

_____

_____

_____

See to it that no one takes you captive through hollow and deceptive philosophy.

Colossians 2:8

Truth 1 | Trapped in the Box

The world has been taken captive by the idea that the cosmos is all that is, ever was, or ever will be.

1. What does Dr. Tackett mean by "assumptive language"? Aside from its use in Carl Sagan's old TV series, what are some more current examples in the popular culture?

_____

_____

_____

2. Do you sense that most people are satisfied to be part of a purely materialistic universe (the "cosmic cube")? Why or why not? What impressions do you get from your non-Christian friends or family members? How do they attempt to cope with life "inside the box"?

_____

_____

_____

Truth 2 | Outside the Box

The Bible says that God actually exists outside the universe. He is not part of it, but He created it and is active within it.

1. Why does it matter that God is not part of "the box" but is independent of it?

_____

_____

_____

_____

2. How important is it to you that God chose to reveal Himself in a special way as well, not just through His creation? What if He had chosen not to intervene in history? Or what if He came to us in Christ but never left a written record of it? Is it possible to take the Bible for granted?

_____

_____

_____

_____

The objects of philosophy are to ascertain facts or truth, and the causes of things or their phenomena; to enlarge our views of God and his works.

Noah Webster, 1828
American Dictionary of the English Language

Truth 3 | It's Dark Inside the Box

When philosophy leaves out God and looks for answers to life only within the natural world, it cannot discover reality.

1. What sort of empty spiritualism do you notice in your community that is being offered as a substitute for belief in a transcendent God? What is its attraction?

_____

_____

_____

_____

2. Was there ever a time in your life when you tried to discover "universal" truths without looking to the Bible for answers? If so, describe your search. How successful were you?

_____

_____

_____

3. Define postmodernism. How should we speak to loved ones who doubt the very existence of objective truth?

_____

_____

_____

_____

Truth 4 | Anarchy in the Box

Without God, there is no basis for ethics. Right and wrong make no sense in a naturalistic universe.

1. Have you ever known a person who genuinely did not believe in any ethical standard? Why is it impossible to live by that belief?

_____

_____

_____

_____

2. How do you differentiate right from wrong? Is the Bible your only guide? What about your conscience (Romans 1:32; 2:14-15)? And what about the Holy Spirit (Galatians 5:16-25)?

_____

_____

_____

_____

3. What does it mean to say that morality is rooted in God's very nature? Why does He want us to reflect His character by our attitudes and behavior (Genesis 1:26-27; 2 Corinthians 3:18; Colossians 3:10; 1 Peter 1:16; 1 John 3:2)?

_____

_____

_____

_____

Truth 5 | Escaping the Box

We are called not just to adopt intellectually a biblical worldview, but also to have our minds renewed so we really believe the realities of which the Bible speaks.

1. Explain what Dr. Tackett meant by your "personal worldview." What are some ways in which your personal worldview is less than biblical?

_____

_____

_____

_____

2. How do we go about having our minds renewed? List some practical steps toward that goal.

_____

_____

_____

_____

_____

3. What sort of people do you think God would like us to be transformed into? Be specific.

_____

_____

_____

_____

Wrap-Up

Even the most outspoken advocates of "cosmic cube" thinking and relativistic ethics cannot live by their own reductionist and materialistic principles. On the other hand, many contemporary Christians have unwittingly become "conformed to this world"—taken captive by the assumptions of our age. So it is imperative that we think more aggressively about what it means to be "transformed by the renewing of your mind" (Romans 12:2).

the first column to its definition in the second column. Terms are found in the lecture or at mytruthproject.org.

1. cosmic cube

   a. scientist and host of "Cosmos" TV series

2. assumptive language

   b. the material world is all that is, was, or ever will be

3. ethics

   c. set of truth claims that purport to describe reality

4. postmodernism

   d. how a person or group of people *should* act

5. formal worldview

   e. present in, but separate from, the created universe

6. Carl Sagan

   f. truth claims that actually drive how we act and feel

7. transcendent

   g. truth derived from nature and natural causes

8. immanent

   h. outside and independent of the material universe

9. personal worldview

   i. statements that hide the key ideas they're based on

10. spiritual naturalism

   j. no single worldview can claim to be the truth

Check It Out

For your reference and further review, here are some of the key Scripture passages that were mentioned in the video you just watched.

Mark 9:2

Romans 12:2

2 Corinthians 3:18

Colossians 2:8

2 Timothy 2:24-26

Anthropology:
Who Is Man?

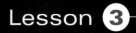

Introduction

Who is man and where did he come from? Is there a meaning or purpose for his existence? Here again we discover a stark contrast between Christianity and our contemporary culture. These two viewpoints also offer very different explanations for the evil we find in ourselves and in the world.

Aside from understanding who God is, nothing could be more important than grasping the truth about human nature. Only by a clear map or picture of what we're made of can we expect to navigate daily life without becoming lost.

TheTruthProject

Quote Unquote

What did they say? Fill in the blanks as you watch this presentation.

1. Of all kinds of knowledge that we can ever obtain, the knowledge of God, and the knowledge of _____, are the most important. —*Jonathan Edwards*

2. The sinful nature desires what is contrary to the _____, and the _____ what is contrary to the sinful nature. —*Galatians 5:17*

3. You cannot slander _____ _____; it is worse than words can paint it. —*C.H. Spurgeon*

4. A rat is a pig is a dog is a _____. —*Ingrid Newkirk*

5. If man is a product of evolution, one species among others, in a universe without purpose, then man's option is to _____ _____ _____. —*Paul Kurtz*

6. The purpose of man is like the purpose of the _____ — to wiggle along as far as he can without dying. —*Clarence Darrow*

7. We are left with the logical conclusion that we are nothing but a _____ man in a _____ universe looking for a _____ brain. —*Del Tackett*

8. As far as I know we just don't have any intrinsic instincts for _____. —*Abraham Maslow*

9. If man is good by nature ..., it follows that he stays like that as long as nothing _____ to him corrupts him. —*Jean-Jacques Rousseau*

10. Experience leads me to believe that it is _____ _____ which are the major factor in our evil behaviors. —*Carl Rogers*

Notes or Questions

While watching the video, use these lines to record your thoughts, any facts you want to remember, questions that arise, etc.

So God created man
in his own image,
in the image of God
he created him.

Genesis 1:27

Truth 1 | Natural Man

Our culture says that man is purely material, the product of mindless forces.

1. People who claim that they are mere accidents of biology still seem driven to find purpose and meaning in life. Why? What keeps them from living according to their beliefs? Why is suicide common today?

_____

_____

_____

2. What presuppositions lie behind the radical environmental movement (not just our common desire to protect nature)? Or behind the animal rights cause? The abortion movement? What other societal trends can you trace to a belief that man is just another product of nature?

_____

_____

_____

Truth 2 | Supernatural Man

The Bible teaches that man consists of both body and spirit and is created in the image of God.

1. What makes man unique in the universe? What does it mean to be made in the image of God?

_____

_____

_____

_____

2. Describe the states of man. Which state are you in? What about friends and family? How concerned are you for those who have not been "redeemed"?

_____

_____

_____

_____

Truth 3 | "Find Yourself"?
The world says that man is naturally good, so evil must derive from the social institutions that stop him from doing what he wants.

1. What evidence can you find that people have bought the concept of man's innocence? How does this lead to a culture of blame and a "victim mentality"?

_____

_____

_____

_____

2. If man is just a product of nature, how can anything be considered evil? What does the world say about this?

_____

_____

_____

3. What solution does society offer to the individual's struggle for fulfillment? How has this pernicious lie worked out? Why are people so hostile to those of us who believe in moral absolutes?

_____

_____

_____

Truth 4 | Deny Yourself

As Christians, we experience an inner conflict between our new nature and the old, fallen nature that causes us to think and do wrong.

1. Are we the people we want to be? Are we able to think and act according to our best intentions? Why or why not? What are some common struggles of Christians today?

_____

_____

_____

2. What can we do to win the battle that rages within? What did the apostle Paul say about it (Romans 7:14-25; 8:13; Colossians 3:5)?

_____

_____

_____

Wrap-Up

How can we humans be so wonderful and so terrible at the same time? In fact, why do we live in a world of both amazing beauty and shocking brutality? And if we are mere products of nature, why do we long for a perfect world in which we can live forever?

Only in the Bible do we find answers to these and other perplexing questions about life—answers that actually help us under-stand ourselves and the world we encounter every day.

Lesson

What Is What?

Here's an exercise to try on your own. Draw a line from each term in the first column to its definition in the second column. Terms are found in the lecture or at mytruthproject.org.

1. imago goo

   a. tap your inner desires to achieve full potential

2. anthropology

   b. innocent, fallen, redeemed, glorified

3. Carl Rogers

   c. the study of mankind's nature and behavior

4. Abraham Maslow

   d. promoter of self-actualization

5. self-actualization

   e. a product of mindless, purposeless forces

6. imago dei

   f. psychologist who said man is basically good

7. monistic

   g. man made in the image of God

8. states of man

   h. made of both natural and supernatural elements

9. dualistic

   i. man is material and has no spiritual dimension

Check It Out

For your reference and further review, here are some of the key Scripture passages that were mentioned in the video you just watched.

Genesis 1:27; 6:5

Romans 5:12; 6:12; 7:14-20,24-25; 8:5-14

1 Corinthians 15:42

Galatians 5:16-17

Colossians 3:5-10

Hebrews 9:27

Revelation 5:9; 20:15

Introduction

No assignment is more daunting, no task more demanding, no challenge more overwhelming, than that of seeking to understand the being, nature, character, and attributes of the eternal Creator, who is Himself the ultimate source of all truth (Colossians 2:3).

But what does it *mean* to "know" Him? And how can we possibly attain such knowledge? This tour focuses on what must be our greatest passion and goal.

TheTruthProject

Quote Unquote

What did they say? Fill in the blanks as you watch this presentation.

1. You and I ought to all be _____. —*Del Tackett*

2. God has not been destroyed. God still exists, but we have cast a
   _____ _____ _____ _____. —*R.C. Sproul*

3. When Jesus is talking about knowing Him, we're talking about an
   _____ knowledge, an _____ understanding,
   an _____ communion. —*Del Tackett*

4. The highest science ... which can engage the attention of a child of
   God is the name, the nature, the person, the doings, and the existence
   of the great God which he calls his _____. —*Charles Spurgeon*

5. Do not worship any other god, for the LORD, whose name is
   _____, is a _____ God. —*Exodus 34:14*

6. When we gaze upon the face of God, we not only begin to know him,
   but we begin to know _____. —*Del Tackett*

7. The two critical questions that we have to address are, first of all, the
   existence of God, and second of all, the _____ _____
   _____ _____. —*R.C. Sproul*

8. How many books in the world have had emperors and empires and
   authorities attempt to _____ it?—*Del Tackett*

9. According to the Jesus Seminar, _____ percent of the words of Jesus
   were not actually spoken by him.—*Del Tackett*

Notes or Questions

While watching the video, use these lines to record your thoughts, any facts you want to remember, questions that arise, etc.

_____

_____

_____

_____

_____

_____

_____

_____

_____

_____

_____

_____

_____

_____

_____

_____

_____

_____

_____

_____

_____

_____

_____

_____

_____

I consider everything
a loss compared to ...
knowing Christ Jesus
my Lord.

Philippians 3:8

Truth 1 | The Greatest Commandment

Nothing in life matters more than knowing and loving God.

1. How did Jesus describe "eternal life," and what does that say about
God's role in our daily existence? Do you like His definition of life, or are
there times when you'd rather be left alone? Explain.

_____

_____

_____

_____

2. What kind(s) of knowledge does God want us to have of Him? Why?
Would you say you are "close" to Him? Explain.

_____

_____

_____

3. Do we live as if relating to Him is more important than anything else we do? Why or why not?

_____

_____

_____

Truth 2 | Thee and Me

Only by relating to God can we discover who we are.

1. What would you know about yourself and your purpose for living if God had not first revealed Himself to you?

_____

_____

_____

2. How does relating intimately to God help you understand yourself? Your neighbor? Your culture?

_____

_____

_____

> **There is but one only living and true God,**
>
> **... the rewarder of them that**
>
> **diligently seek him.**
>
> The Westminster Confession of Faith

Truth 3 | The Bible Tells Me So

We must study God's Word in order to understand more about His nature and to "gaze into His face."

1. Why has God's written word always been under intense attack by the world? What are some recent examples you've observed?

_____

_____

_____

2. Do you hunger and thirst for more knowledge of God through studying and obeying the Scriptures—or do you often feel as though you've "been there, done that"? Why? What would you like to do differently?

_____

_____

_____

All Scripture is God-breathed and is useful for teaching, rebuking, correcting and training in righteousness.

2 Timothy 3:16

Wrap-Up

Discovering God's holy character cannot help but reveal to us our own fallen nature, so that we are compelled to cry, "Woe is me, for I am undone!" (Isaiah 6:5).

But then, as He raises us out of our despair and shows us who we can be in Him, we are granted the gift of a new name—a whole new understanding of our being, our identity, and our purpose in life with God. The fruit of this experience is personal transformation.

Here's an exercise to try on your own. Draw a line from each term in the first column to its definition in the second column. Terms are found in the lecture or at mytruthproject.org.

1. El Qanna

    a. to know the only true God, and Jesus whom He sent

2. Jesus Seminar

    b. "god" is present in everything

3. theism

    c. scholar who proposed the Documentary Hypothesis

4. Julius Wellhausen

    d. "There is but one only, living, and true God …"

5. eternal life

    e. God created and governs the world of man and nature

6. theology

    f. studying the existence, nature, and attributes of God

7. deism

Check It Out

For your reference and further review, here are some of the key Scripture passages that were mentioned in the video you just watched.

Exodus 34:10-17

Deuteronomy 4:23-24

Psalm 42:1-2

Jeremiah 9:23-24

Hosea 6:6

Zechariah 8:2

John 3:16; 4:13-14; 5:24,39-40;
6:27,54; 17:1-3

2 Corinthians 10:4-5

Philippians 3:8-10

Colossians 2:1-3

Science:

Introduction

Everywhere we look—whether up at the grandeur of the stars or deep into the workings of a living cell—we come face to face with the God who has revealed Himself not only through His written Word but also through the works of His hands.

But mankind does not react to this evidence the way we'd hoped. In this tour, we'll examine that response and discover why it's becoming even harder today to deny the existence of God.

TheTruthProject

Quote Unquote

What did they say? Fill in the blanks as you watch this presentation.

1. Since the creation of the world God's invisible qualities—his
   _____ _____ and _____ _____—
   have been clearly seen, being understood from what has been made.
   —Romans 1:19-20

2. Given so much _____ , the impossible becomes possible."
   —George Wald

3. The chief aim of all investigations of the external world should be
   to discover the _____ _____ and _____
   which has been imposed on it by God. *—Johannes Kepler*

4. Darwinianism has come of age so to speak. We are no longer having to
   bother about establishing the _____ of evolution. *—Julian Huxley*

5. Biology is the study of complicated things that give the _____
   of having been designed for a purpose. *—Richard Dawkins*

6. The sight of a feather in a _____ _____, whenever I gaze at it, makes me sick! *—Charles Darwin*

7. Evolution is a fact amply demonstrated by the _____ _____
   and by contemporary molecular biology. *—Carl Sagan*

8. What we're now discovering is that the cell is chock-full of exquisite
   miniature _____. *—Stephen Meyer*

9. Evolution destroys utterly and finally the very reason _____
   _____ _____ was supposedly made necessary.
   —G. Richard Bozarth

Notes or Questions

While watching the video, use these lines to record your thoughts, any facts you want to remember, questions that arise, etc.

_____

_____

_____

_____

_____

_____

_____

_____

_____

_____

_____

_____

_____

_____

_____

_____

_____

_____

_____

_____

_____

_____

_____

_____

_____

Science: **What Is True?**

> The heavens declare
> the glory of God;
> the skies proclaim
> the work of his hands.
>
> Psalm 19:1

Truth 1 | Plain as Day (and Night Too)

According to the Bible, God has revealed His glorious nature in the universe He created.

1. What are some specific things in the physical world that fill you with awe? What do they tell you about the Creator?

_____

_____

_____

_____

2. How difficult is it for us to view nature (a rainbow, for example) as we once did? Does that matter? How might we restore our childlike sense of wonder at God's creation?

_____

_____

_____

Truth 2 | Science Started with God

The scientific revolution began with the assumption that the world had been divinely created in an orderly way and could therefore be studied.

1. How do you feel about the fact that early science was primarily a Christian response to the world around us? How might that encourage you when you see science being used today as an argument *against* the faith?

_____

_____

_____

2. In what way can scientific research be an act of worship?

_____

_____

_____

3. Which early scientist(s) might you want to learn more about? You can often read their very own works, not just biographies about them.

_____

_____

_____

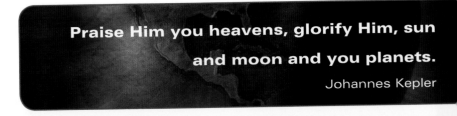

Praise Him you heavens, glorify Him, sun and moon and you planets.

Johannes Kepler

Truth 3 | A Stronger Case Than Ever

Today we have new evidence pointing to God's design of the universe.

1. What are some key things we understand about the night sky that we didn't know even a hundred years ago? Which objects might you want to locate there with binoculars or the naked eye?

_____

_____

_____

2. What do you think of the scientific evidence that suggests the universe has not always existed?

_____

_____

_____

3. Explain in your own words what has been discovered about the inner workings of the cell and the information contained in DNA. How is this like finding a wristwatch in the field while out on a walk? What other evidences of design in nature impress you or make you want to investigate further?

_____

_____

_____

Truth 4 | The Blind Eye and Deaf Ear

Modern science refuses to follow the evidence where it leads and instead treats alternative theories about the universe as fact.

1. Why did Einstein and other scientists want to believe that the world had always been here? What discovery spoiled their hopes? How do you feel about scientists who are driven more by their religious or philosophical worldview than by scientific data?

_____

_____

_____

_____

2. Suppose you were talking to someone who thought Darwin's theory of evolution explained life on earth. What evidence (or *lack* of evidence) in modern science would you mention to call evolution into doubt?

_____

_____

_____

Biologists must constantly keep in mind that what they see was not designed, but rather evolved.

Francis Crick

3. What are some ways that scientists have responded to evidence for intelligent design in the cell? How might you review or study the evidence further so that you can share it with others?

_____

_____

_____

_____

_____

_____

_____

_____

_____

I believe that one day the Darwinian myth will be ranked the greatest deceit in the history of science.

Soren Lovtrup
Darwinism: The Refutation of a Myth

Wrap-Up

We've seen how fallen man ignores the plain evidence of objective scientific inquiry and promotes the atheistic philosophy of evolution primarily because he is determined to act as he pleases without answering to a higher authority.

Does this hit close to home? Are we, as Christians, sometimes inclined to live our own lives without asking the Lord for His power and direction?

Here's an exercise to try on your own. Draw a line from each term in the first column to its definition in the second column. Terms are found in the lecture or at mytruthproject.org.

1. irreducible complexity

  a. microorganisms came to earth from outer space

2. fossil record

  b. co-discoverer of DNA who rejected evidence of design

3. directed panspermia

  c. author of *Icons of Evolution*

4. punctuated equilibrium

  d. like a mousetrap, needs every part in order to work

5. Francis Crick

  e. early assumption made using limited evidence

6. hypothesis

  f. remains of plants and animals

Check It Out

For your reference and further review, here are some of the key Scripture passages that were mentioned in the video you just watched.

Genesis 1—2

Psalm 8; 19; 111; 139:13-16

Amos 5:8

Acts 14:16-17

Romans 1:20

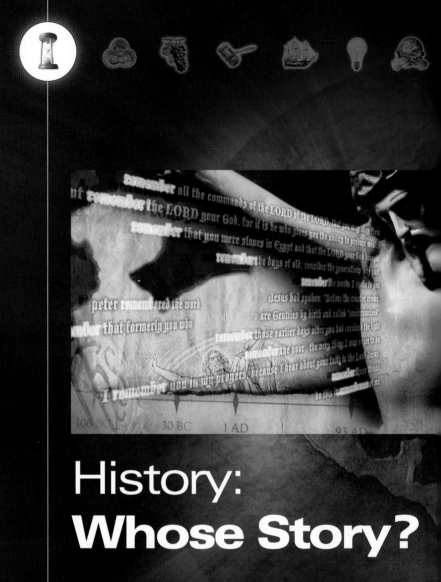

History:
Whose Story?

Introduction

History provides us with indispensable insights into the meaning of existence and God's plan and purpose for the ages. God is absolutely in control, and history is His story. The details of our lives are mere threads in the great tapestry of His overarching plan.

Hence we are enjoined to "remember the former things, those of long ago; I am God, and there is no other " (Isaiah 46:9). If we do not recall what He has done, we run the risk of becoming myopic, proud, and clueless when we try to put our lives in perspective.

TheTruthProject

Quote Unquote

What did they say? Fill in the blanks as you watch this presentation.

1. In the name of God, Amen. We, whose names are underwritten, … having undertaken for the glory of God, and _____ of the _____ _____, … a voyage to plant the first colony … —*Mayflower Compact*

2. If you can rewrite the _____, you can make people believe whatever you want in the _____. —*Del Tackett*

3. He who _____ the past, _____ the future. —*George Orwell*

4. We have a tendency to _____ the things we're supposed to _____, and to _____ the things we're supposed to _____. —*Del Tackett*

5. If you don't have a certain knowledge of history, then you can't understand anything about the _____ _____. —*Theodore Dalrymple*

6. Those who don't know history have no sense of _____ and no sense of _____ as they explore where they're gonna go. Without history, we're lost. —*Os Guinness*

7. Be careful that you do not _____ the LORD your God, failing to observe his commands, his laws and his decrees that I am giving you this day. —*Deuteronomy 8:11*

8. The _____ of the LORD stand firm forever, the _____ of his heart through all generations. —*Psalm 33:11*

9. Simplifying to the extreme, I define postmodern as incredulity towards _____. —*Jean-Francois Lyotard*

Notes or Questions

While watching the video, use these lines to record your thoughts, any facts you want to remember, questions that arise, etc.

_____

_____

_____

_____

_____

_____

_____

_____

_____

_____

_____

_____

_____

_____

_____

_____

_____

_____

_____

_____

_____

_____

"Remember the
former things,
those of long ago;
I am God, and
there is no other."

Isaiah 46:9

Truth 1 | History Matters

*Knowing what happened in the past helps us understand the present
and then act accordingly.*

1. What would you do if you woke up tomorrow morning and couldn't
remember anything about your past? Really try to imagine having amnesia.
How important is your personal history?

_____

_____

_____

2. How would you rate your knowledge of history in general? Of Western
civilization? In what ways might a better understanding of the past help
you in life?

_____

_____

_____

3. Which sources of historical information appeal you to most? Books? Video documentaries? Biography? Historical fiction? Letters? Other original documents?

_____

_____

_____

_____

Truth 2 | Time to Rewrite?

Revising history and casting doubt on God's Word are old tactics of those who oppose us.

1. What book, textbook, or video documentary do you know about that seems to rewrite a part of history? How best can you alert others to all the misinformation out there?

_____

_____

_____

_____

2. Why do you think the Bible's historical accuracy is always being challenged? Have those attacks in any way diminished your confidence in Scripture? What do we know about the formation of the Bible that should give you great comfort?

_____

_____

_____

_____

Truth 3 | Join in God's Story

Life is not about us but about God's sovereign plan for redeeming mankind. We should remember His past actions and participate in His grand purpose.

1. Whether out loud or in writing, try telling the entire story of the Bible, from beginning to end, in your own words. If you find that too difficult, which parts of "salvation history" do you need to brush up on?

_____

_____

_____

_____

2. How would you rate your knowledge of what God has done through His people in the centuries that followed Jesus' time on earth? How would you like to improve your understanding of church history? How would that be helpful to you?

_____

_____

_____

_____

3. Are we living out mostly our own stories, or are we participating in God's larger story? What might that mean in practical terms? What is He calling us to do?

_____

_____

_____

Wrap-Up

From beginning to end, Dr. Tackett's message in this tour is that "it's not all about you." As Jesus put it, "He who seeks to save his life will lose it." If, instead, life is all about God, we need to know what He has been up to over the millennia.

But according to Os Guinness, "Many Christians have an abominable view of the past"—meaning that they don't grasp the importance of knowing what has gone before. Is this a weakness in your life? Are you living out of context? Few things matter more than becoming part of God's larger story.

What Is What?

Here's an exercise to try on your own. Draw a line from each term in the first column to its definition in the second column. Terms are found in the lecture or at mytruthproject.org.

1. metanarrative

a. reinterpreting the past to change views of the present

2. historical revisionism

b. philosophy or worldview that seeks to explain reality

3. natural myopia

c. sweeping plan to bring out God's eternal purposes

4. paradoxical

d. having supreme authority or power

5. sovereign

e. governor of Plymouth Colony

6. larger story of God

f. governor of Judea in first century A.D.

7. free agents

g. seemingly absurd or contradictory but possibly true

8. William Bradford

h. wisdom, guidance, and control provided by God

9. Pontius Pilate

i. individuals who make independent choices

10. providence

j. focusing on our own life, ignoring larger world

Check It Out

For your reference and further review, here are some of the key Scripture passages that were mentioned in the video you just watched.

Joshua 4:1-7

Numbers 15:38-39

Deuteronomy 4:9; 6:4-12; 8:10-20

Psalm 33:10-11

Isaiah 46:8-11

Matthew 28:11-15

Ephesians 1:11

Sociology: **The Divine Imprint**

Introduction

From the atom to the solar system, from a chicken egg to the human body—everywhere we discover purposeful design in the *material* things God has made. But the same element of order is apparent in the *social* systems He has instituted.

Dr. Tackett identifies six social spheres from Scripture: family, labor, church, state, community, and the relationship between man and his Maker. Let's begin looking at these, giving special attention on this tour to the family.

TheTruthProject

Quote Unquote

What did they say? Fill in the blanks as you watch this presentation.

1. Our God has _____ and _____ within His
    own being. —*R.C. Sproul*

2. In the unity of the Godhead there be three persons, of one
    _____, power, and eternity: God the Father, God the
    Son, and God the Holy Ghost. —*Westminster Confession*

3. God did not sit in heaven and dream up something called [the]
    "_____ _____." —*Del Tackett*

4. Within the _____ nature of God, we have everything. Every-
    thing! Intimacy. Union. Communion. Fellowship. Love. Community.
    —*Del Tackett*

5. Social order is bound up in the nature of God, because He created
    social institutions with the _____ _____ of who
    He is. —*Del Tackett*

6. Wives, submit to your husbands as to the Lord. For the husband is the
    _____ of the wife as Christ is the _____ of the church, his
    body, of which he is the Savior. —*Ephesians 5:22*

7. Be _____ of the church of God, which he bought
    with his own blood. —*Acts 20:28*

Notes or Questions

While watching the video, use these lines to record your thoughts, any facts you want to remember, questions that arise, etc.

"Dominion and awe belong to God; he establishes order in the heights of heaven."

Job 25:2

Truth 1 | God's Social Networks

Our basic social institutions, including the family and the church, did not just evolve but were created by God.

1. How well can you back up this statement with Scripture? (Hint: See "Check It Out" on p. 79.) Or with other evidence?

_____

_____

_____

2. How would your life be different if there were no social order—no family to belong to, no churches, no governmental or community structures—but just you, on your own? Imagine and describe a typical day or week.

_____

_____

_____

_____

Truth 2 | The Stamp of God

The family as God designed it reflects His own nature. The church does so as well.

1. In what ways do marriage and family mirror the character of God? Describe what you see happening whenever people try to change the design He intended.

_____

_____

_____

_____

2. What should it mean in practical terms that Christ is head of His body, the church?

_____

_____

_____

> **"For this reason a man will leave his father and mother and be united to his wife...."** This is a profound mystery—but I am talking about Christ and the church.
>
> Ephesians 5:31-32

Truth 3 | Under Attack

The world's hostility toward God lies behind its war against the family and other institutions He created.

1. Do you believe the family is under attack? If so, in what ways? What can happen when one social institution tries to supersede another rather than stay within divinely ordered bounds? Give some examples.

_____

_____

_____

2. What societal problems can be traced back to the breakdown of God's social order? Which of these problems most concern you, and what can we do about them?

_____

_____

_____

If we could hear but for a brief instant what God must hear in this realm of the pathology of the family, it would crush us.

Del Tackett

Wrap-Up

We've seen that the social order is not simply an expression of the Lord's creative design, but that it also flows out of His very being. It is a reflection of who He is—diversity within unity. Further, His triune nature explains why it is "not good for man to be alone."

Do you know anyone who is alone? Maybe alone even when part of a church? If so, what is the Lord calling you to do about it? The world's crusade against God's social order should be countered by the daily actions of every believer.

What Is What?

Here's an exercise to try on your own. Draw a line from each term in the first column to its definition in the second column. Terms are found in the lecture or at mytruthproject.org.

1. submission

2. Intimate Three

3. order

4. divine imprint

5. system

6. social spheres

7. Trinity

8. social order

a. reflection of God's character and communal nature

b. elements arranged properly, neatly, or harmoniously

c. related elements organized into a complex whole

d. Father, Son, and Holy Spirit, each fully God

e. willingness to operate under the authority of another

f. family, church, God and man, state, labor, and community

g. God and man, family, and church

h. God's design of institutions and their function in society

Check It Out

For your reference and further review, here are some of the key Scripture passages that were mentioned in the video you just watched.

Genesis 1:26-28; 2:18-24

Exodus 20:12,14,17

Malachi 2:13-17

Matthew 19:4-8

Acts 20:28

1 Corinthians 14:33

Ephesians 5:22-33; 6:1-4

Colossians 3:18-21

Titus 1:5-6; 2:4-5

Hebrews 13:4,17

1 Peter 3:1-7

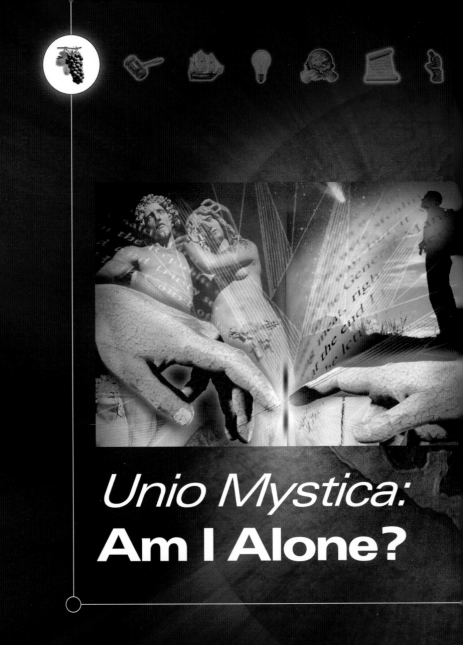

Unio Mystica:
Am I Alone?

Introduction

In this tour we have the privilege of pondering exactly what it is that Christ has purchased for us on the Cross: not simply salvation from hell, but also an invitation into a mystical union (the Latin is *unio mystica*) with God.

This profound mystery lies at the heart not only of corporate church life, but also of the individual believer's everyday experience. Here, Dr. Tackett says, is the greatest of all the wonders to contemplate: that the God of the universe has chosen to make His dwelling with us and in us.

TheTruthProject

Quote Unquote

What does Scripture say? Fill in the blanks as you watch this presentation.

1. Before long, the world will not see me anymore, but you will see me.
    Because I _____, you also will _____. —*John 14:19*

2. I am the vine; you are the branches. If a man_____ in me and I in him,
    he will bear much fruit; apart from me you can do nothing. —*John 15:5*

3. And I will ask the Father, and he will give you another _____
    to be with you forever—the Spirit of truth. —*John 14:16-17*

4. In him you too are being built together to become a _____
    in which God lives by his Spirit. —*Ephesians 2:22*

5. I have given them the _____ that you gave me, that they may
    be one as we are one: I in them and you in me. —*John 17:22-23*

6. There is _____ body and _____ Spirit—just as you were called to
    _____ hope when you were called— _____ Lord, _____ faith,
    _____ baptism. —*Ephesians 4:3-5*

7. A new command I give you: _____ _____ _____. As I have loved
    you, so you must _____ _____ _____. By this all men will know
    that you are my disciples, if you _____ _____ _____. —*John 13:34-35*

8. When you give to the needy, do not let your left hand know what your right
    hand is doing, so that your giving may be ____ _____. Then your Father,
    who sees what is done ____ _____, will reward you. —*Matthew 6:3-4*

9. As the deer _____ for streams of water, so my soul _____ for
    you, O God. My soul thirsts for God, for the living God. —*Psalm 42:1-2*

Notes or Questions

While watching the video, use these lines to record your thoughts, any facts you want to remember, questions that arise, etc.

_____

_____

_____

_____

_____

_____

_____

_____

_____

_____

_____

_____

_____

_____

_____

_____

_____

_____

_____

_____

_____

_____

Unio Mystica: **Am I Alone?**

> "You know him,
> for he lives with you
> and will be in you."
>
> John 14:17

Truth 1 | One on One

God has called each of us into an intimate relationship with Him.

1. In what way does being saved go beyond merely escaping the final judgment and entering eternal life? God "saves" us for what purpose?

_____

_____

_____

_____

2. Describe your present relationship with God. Would you call it intimate? Distant? Neither? How much of your relationship has to do with "hearing His voice" and sensing His love, not just intellectually knowing *about* Him?

_____

_____

_____

_____

3. What measures can we take to grow closer to the Lord? Are there regular practices or disciplines that would help us "abide" in Him? What might a plan of action look like?

_____

_____

_____

Truth 2 | Together with Him

God has called us to form one body, the church, that is intimately related to Him.

1. Why is there no such thing as individual Christianity? Have you tried to follow Christ alone? In what ways do we need others in our endeavor to obey the Lord?

_____

_____

_____

2. What does God want believers to do *for* and *with* one another? Pick your favorite New Testament epistle (such as Colossians or 1 Peter) and highlight every command God gave to His people in that letter. Which of them are you doing faithfully, at least among your closest friends and family members? Which commands would you like to work on more?

_____

_____

_____

3. Why is it important not to let our own relationship to God become a substitute for involvement with other Christians in the church, or vice versa? If you have ever made this mistake, what was the result?

_____

_____

_____

Truth 3 | Barriers to Intimacy

We distance ourselves from the Lord and from one another whenever we strive for personal significance instead of finding God's love sufficient.

1. What keeps us from deeper intimacy with God? Scrambling to "make a mark" in life? Pursuing wealth or success or popularity? Other distractions or misplaced priorities? Let the Lord speak to you as you consider this. What would He have us do differently?

_____

_____

_____

_____

2. What keeps the church from oneness and unity in Christ, both locally and on a larger scale? When are doctrinal differences handled wrongly?

_____

_____

_____

_____

3. If the local church is really about relationships (per the "one another" commands in Scripture), where can you find your best opportunities to connect with and help other believers in a significant way?

_____

_____

_____

_____

Wrap-Up

Christianity is not primarily a moral or religious system, but rather an intimate and personal relationship with our Creator. But such a relationship can grow deeper only when we know what He desires from us and then do it.

As Jesus said, "Whoever has my commands and obeys them, he is the one who loves me. He who loves me will be loved by my Father, and I too will love him and *show myself to him*" (John 14:21, emphasis added). We should constantly reread Scripture so that we can hear afresh and follow His commands.

Check It Out

For your reference and further review, here are some of the key Scripture passages that were mentioned in the video you just watched.

Psalm 42:1-2

Isaiah 55:1-2

Matthew 6:1-18

John 13:34-35; 14:16-21;
15:5-12; 17:3,20-23

Romans 12:4-5,10,16;
14:19; 15:5,7

2 Corinthians 5:17

Galatians 2:20; 6:2

Ephesians 1:9-10;
2:19-22; 4:3-5,11-14,32;
5:21,31-32

Philippians 2:3

Colossians 1:27; 3:16

1 Thessalonians 4:18;
5:11

James 5:16

1 Peter 1:22

The State:
Whose Law?

Introduction

The government can exert a tremendous power for good in the affairs of mankind. But it also has the potential to become the most horrendously abusive of all the social spheres.

In this tour, we explore this dual nature of the divinely instituted state. When and why does something meant for good become so bad? And how should Christians respond?

TheTruthProject

Quote Unquote

What did they say? Fill in the blanks as you watch this presentation.

1. This sphere can become the most _____ _____ of all. And I think that is the reason why God continues to remind the king that he is subject to God. —*Del Tackett*

2. All around the world and throughout history, you can see the _____ that have been committed by this sphere. —*Del Tackett*

3. Darwin had said that if his naturalistic framework were taken as a scaffolding for metaphysical extrapolations ..., the _____ that would break out would be unparalleled. —*Ravi Zacharias*

4. Almost 170 million men, women and children have been shot, beaten, tortured, ... or killed in any other of a myriad of ways [that] _____ have inflicted death on unarmed, helpless citizens and foreigners. —*R.J. Rummel*

5. Without truth, there is only _____. —*Os Guinness*

6. Experience leads me to believe that it is _____ _____ which are the major factor in our evil behaviors. —*Carl Rogers*

7. If there is no _____ truth, if there are no _____ standards, then it's okay for me to live however I want to live. —*R.C. Sproul*

8. The welfare state has become the nanny state. And I think that is very sad, to see the state substitute itself for the _____. —*Robert Sirico*

9. We have reached the turning point in human history where the best option is to transcend the limits of _____ _____. —*Humanist Manifesto II*

Notes or Questions

While watching the video, use these lines to record your thoughts, any facts you want to remember, questions that arise, etc.

Everyone must
submit himself
to the governing
authorities.

Romans 13:1

Truth 1 | Render unto Caesar

The state (that is, government in general) is a social sphere established by God to exercise control under His authority.

1. Look around you. What are the benefits of government? How would you feel living in a society that had no laws or law enforcement? No building codes or maintained roads? No national defense?

_____

_____

_____

2. The Bible tells us to "honor the emperor" (1 Peter 2:17). How do we obey that command while also facing the truth about who many of our leaders are today? What examples come to mind from Scripture?

_____

_____

_____

Truth 2 | What Is Caesar's

God meant for the state's authority to be limited, not extending into other social spheres such as the church or the family.

1. How would you describe or limit the sphere that the state is charged to manage? See Romans 13:1-7 and related passages. In what areas should we submit to the government?

_____

_____

_____

2. What are some current debates in politics and society that stem from a disagreement over the scope of the state's responsibilities?

_____

_____

_____

We must therefore worship the State as the manifestation of the Divine on earth....
The State is the march of God through the world.

Georg Wilhelm Friedrich Hegel

Truth 3 | In a Terrible State

When the state no longer recognizes God as its higher authority, it can (and often does) become a fearsome monster.

1. What historical examples come to mind in which the state expanded greatly beyond its appointed sphere? What happened as a result? Where is this still happening today, either in relatively minor or in serious, life-threatening ways? How can we help support Christians who live under the rule of a monster state?

_____

_____

_____

_____

2. When is it wrong to accept benefits or supposed protections offered by a "nanny state"? What should the church do when the state takes on responsibilities that ought to be handled by the church or other private institutions?

_____

_____

_____

_____

3. In what ways is the state a threat to the family? How has the growth of the state over time changed the way that families used to work? What should we do about it?

_____

_____

_____

Wrap-Up

The unfettered expansion of state power has reared its ugly head many times in the past, most notably in the 20th-century regimes of Lenin, Stalin, Hitler, Mao, and Pol Pot. It is raising its head again in our own time.

Without God, truth, or any higher moral standard, people are increasingly looking to the state as savior and the supplier of every human need. In the face of this trend, Bible-believing Christians must have the courage to resist the rise of the state.

Check It Out

For your reference and further review, here are some of the key Scripture passages that were mentioned in the video you just watched.

Exodus 22:28	Proverbs 21:1
Deuteronomy 17:16-20	Luke 20:25
1 Samuel 8:1-20	John 17:1-2
1 Kings 21:1-19	Acts 17:24-26
2 Chronicles 20:6; 26:1-23	Romans 9:17; 12:17-21; 13:1-7
Daniel 2:21; 4:29-36	1 Corinthians 15:24-28
Job 12:23	Titus 3:1
Psalm 2:1-3; 22:28	1 Peter 2:13-17
	Revelation 13

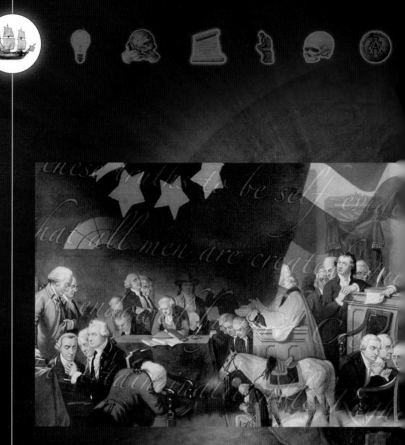

The American Experiment:
Stepping Stones

Introduction

Before we leave the subject of the state, we're going to examine a particular example, asking, "What is a proper form for this agency that is divinely appointed to administer justice, punish evil, and encourage goodness among its citizens or subjects?"

In the founding of America, people with a strong Christian worldview were afforded an unparalleled opportunity to create from scratch what they considered an ideal system of government. After we study how the American Experiment began with promise, we'll see how it has gone terribly wrong.

TheTruthProject

Quote Unquote

What did they say? Fill in the blanks as you watch this presentation.

1. *Faith in the prayer-hearing God is an _____ and _____ faith.* —John Dewey

2. *Cursed is all learning that is contrary to the _____ __ _____.* —Princeton's Founding Statement, 1746

3. *In my view, the _____ _____ is the most important and one of the first things in which all children, under a free government, ought to be instructed.* —Noah Webster

4. *Of all the dispositions and habits which lead to political prosperity, _____ and _____ are indispensable supports.* —George Washington

5. *Religion and good morals are the only solid foundations of public liberty and _____.* —Samuel Adams

6. *The Americans combine the notions of Christianity and _____ so intimately in their minds that it is impossible to make them conceive one without the other.* —Alexis de Tocqueville

7. *Only a virtuous people are capable of _____. As nations become corrupt and vicious, they have more need of masters.* —Benjamin Franklin

8. *Our _____ was made only for a moral and religious people. It is wholly inadequate to the government of any other.* —John Adams

9. *There is no guarantee that I'm aware of in the Bible or anywhere else that this _____, which has produced so much good for so many people, will continue to exist.* —Robert Sirico

Notes or Questions

While watching the video, use these lines to record your thoughts, any facts you want to remember, questions that arise, etc.

_____

_____

_____

_____

_____

_____

_____

_____

_____

_____

_____

_____

_____

_____

_____

_____

_____

_____

_____

_____

_____

_____

"When I fed them,
they were satisfied;
when they were
satisfied, they
became proud."

Hosea 13:6

Truth 1 | Built on the Rock

America was founded by people who held to a comprehensive biblical worldview.

1. Were you surprised by all the evidence showing how profoundly Christian most of America's founders were? How much of this had you already been exposed to in high school or college?

_____

_____

_____

_____

2. Do you believe that America was in some way created by God Himself, or rather that it was just formed by the good intentions of some of His followers? What did the founders say about America's birth? Why?

_____

_____

_____

3. How did a Christian worldview lead the founders to adopt the structure of federal government that America still enjoys today? Why is it important for each branch to hold separate powers?

_____

_____

_____

Truth 2 | A Nation Adrift

In the late 1800s, America began a long journey away from its founding beliefs and principles.

1. Why did John Adams say that "our Constitution was made only for a moral and religious people. It is wholly inadequate to the government of any other"? Where does that leave us today?

_____

_____

_____

2. What happens when law becomes based merely on precedent and on society's current notions of right and wrong rather than on biblical principles and the law of nature? When you read about a trial in the news today, how much difference do you detect between what is deemed legal and what is morally right or just?

_____

_____

_____

3. Why do you think it is in vogue today to hate America? How much of it is a response to America's religious roots, and how much of it is a reaction to the nation's drift away from Christian principles?

_____

_____

_____

Truth 3 | "If My People ..."

Christians must not abandon America but rather pray and work hard for a return to biblical roots.

1. Is it *necessary* for a nation to go through the cycle of being blessed by God, then forgetting Him, enduring His judgment, and finally repenting so as to be blessed again? What hopes, if any, do you have that America might return full-circle to its roots? If you are an American, what can you do toward that end?

_____

_____

_____

_____

2. How would you describe the church's impact on American culture today? Have Christians lost their ability to be a preserving "salt" in the world? A light in the darkness? If so, what must we do to regain influence in our multicultural society?

_____

_____

_____

_____

3. Do you have a heart for America? A passion for the ideals on which it was founded? How might you, or your friends, have been influenced by those who view America with disdain? How do you think God feels about this nation today?

_____

_____

_____

Wrap-Up

Today, America has largely forgotten God and denied the validity of her biblical roots. As a result, we see the power of the state expanding. This is a manifestation of the perennial cosmic battle, which is fought most fiercely in the social realm.

Ultimately, we must face the fact that the American Experiment is likely to fail altogether if we do not take intentional and deliberate steps to salvage it. Just as the experiment was instigated by Christians, so it must be carried on by believers who care deeply and passionately about their country.

What Is What?

Here's an exercise to try on your own. Draw a line from each term in the first column to its definition in the second column. Terms are found in the lecture or at mytruthproject.org.

1. George Washington

2. Noah Webster

3. de Tocqueville

4. Thomas Jefferson

5. *New England Primer*

6. natural law

7. case study method

8. American Experiment

9. United States Constitution

10. legal positivism

a. principal author of the Declaration of Independence

b. political thinker who wrote *Democracy in America*

c. first president of the United States.

d. law fundamental to human nature rather than invented

e. "the father of American education"

f. law that evolves through previous court decisions

g. law shaped by the state rather than a higher authority

h. attempt to establish a nation built on biblical principles

i. document that created a union of sovereign states

j. early textbook that taught children how to read

Check It Out

For your reference and further review, here are some of the key Scripture passages that were mentioned in the video you just watched.

Deuteronomy 8:10-20

2 Chronicles 7:13-14

Isaiah 33:22

Hosea 13:6

Romans 13:1-6

Revelation 2:5

Labor: **Created to Create**

Introduction

Do you like to work, or do you dread it? Perhaps both? In this tour, we discover why our daily labors can produce both pleasure and pain.

Work is not a "curse," as many people might say, but an essential element of our humanity, rooted in the very nature of God. It is not just something we have to do for money. Yet in our fallen world, work does sometimes present challenges.

Let's look closer at God's perspective on the role of labor and finances in our lives.

TheTruthProject

Quote Unquote

What does Scripture say? Fill in the blanks as you watch this presentation.

1. "Six days you shall labor and do all your work, but the seventh day is a _____ of the LORD your God." —*Exodus 20:9-10 (NAS)*

2. "Cursed is the ground because of you; through _____ toil you will eat of it all the days of your life."—*Genesis 3:17*

3. "Every animal of the forest is mine, and the _____ on a thousand hills…. If I were hungry I would not tell you, for the world is mine, and all that is in it."—*Psalm 50:7-12*

4. God blessed them and said to them, "Be fruitful and increase in number; fill the earth and _____ it." —*Genesis 1:28*

5. Serve wholeheartedly, as if you were serving the _____, not men, because you know that the _____ will reward everyone for whatever good he does. —*Ephesians 6:5-8*

6. All hard work brings a profit, but mere talk leads only to _____. —*Proverbs 14:23*

7. "No one can serve two masters. Either he will hate the one and love the other, or he will be devoted to the one and despise the other. You cannot serve both God and _____." —*Matthew 6:24*

8. If anyone has material possessions and sees his brother in need but has no pity on him, how can the _____ ____ _____ be in him? —*1 John 3:17*

Notes or Questions

While watching the video, use these lines to record your thoughts, any facts you want to remember, questions that arise, etc.

_____

_____

_____

_____

_____

_____

_____

_____

_____

_____

_____

_____

_____

_____

_____

_____

_____

_____

_____

_____

_____

_____

_____

_____

_____

_____

The LORD God took the man and put him in the Garden of Eden to work it.

Genesis 2:15

Truth 1 | One Creator, Many Sub-Creators

God made us in His image, so we too like to work and create things.

1. Clearly, the Lord enjoyed creating the world. So what kind of work do you enjoy? Would you rather do that work than simply pursue recreation every day? For you, when does work become play?

_____

_____

_____

2. How would your life be different if other people did not build roads or construct buildings, write books, invent cars or computers, grow food, provide health care, create music (or paintings or photographs), etc.? What is it that you were created to create? Are you regularly engaged in that work? Why or why not? What will it take to devote yourself more to God's particular calling?

_____

_____

_____

3. Do you "observe the Sabbath" (or "the Lord's Day")? Why or why not? If you do, *how* do you observe it? Are you glad to do so, seeing rest as a gift from God? Or is your Sunday filled with work, much like other days?

_____

_____

_____

Truth 2 | Work Takes Work

After man rebelled against God, work became harder, but it is still a good thing, and we should enjoy being stewards for God.

1. Do we really believe that everything ultimately belongs to God, including all that we own? Do we *act* as faithful stewards of God's things? Does that include our talents and abilities? Our bodies? Our time?

_____

_____

_____

2. How do you feel about work? Do you dread Monday morning? If so, why? Do you think that you *have* to work, or rather that you *get* to work? Has your attitude toward work been distorted by the world's perspective?

_____

_____

_____

3. How should you respond when your job is mundane, demeaning, overly stressful, or a burden in some other way?

_____

_____

_____

The Bible contains many principles that should govern how we go about being stewards for God.

1. Do we freely give to others in need, as God would have us do? How can we help the poor find fulfilling work, not just "welfare" (a handout)? Why is that an important distinction?

_____

_____

_____

2. Does all your work, no matter what field you're in, glorify God? What is the difference between "sacred" and "secular" work?

_____

_____

_____

3. Which sources of information and entertainment are most important to us? Do they offer the truth or lies? Do the lies bother us, or do they sometimes amuse us?

_____

_____

_____

4. How do you view retirement? What is your dream for your senior years? Is that just your goal, or is it God's wish for you as well?

_____

_____

_____

Wrap-Up

Having an unbiblical understanding of labor is a sure way to make your work week miserable. If you don't want merely to live for the weekends, as so many do, it's important that you recognize what a gift God has given us in the field of labor.

Few things in this life are more satisfying than productive, creative work, and even in the New Earth (2 Peter 3:13) we can look forward to the enjoyable task of managing God's creation (Genesis 1:26-28; 2:15). So if you have a "TGIF" attitude toward work, it's time to see it God's way.

Check It Out

For your reference and further review, here are some of the key Scripture passages that were mentioned in the video you just watched.

Genesis 1:26-30; 2:2, 15; 3:17-19

Exodus 20:8-11,15,17; 23:11

Leviticus 19:9-10; 25:23

Deuteronomy 8:17-18; 24:15

Psalm 19:1; 50:7-12; 101:3; 102:25

Proverbs 6:6-11; 10:4; 14:23; 22:29; 28:27; 29:7

Matthew 6:20-24; 25:14-30

Mark 2:27

Luke 12:48

2 Corinthians 8:13-15

Ephesians 4:28; 6:5-9

Colossians 3:22-25; 4:1

2 Thessalonians 3:10

1 Timothy 6:1-2

Titus 2:9-10

James 5:4

1 Peter 2:18-22

1 John 3:17

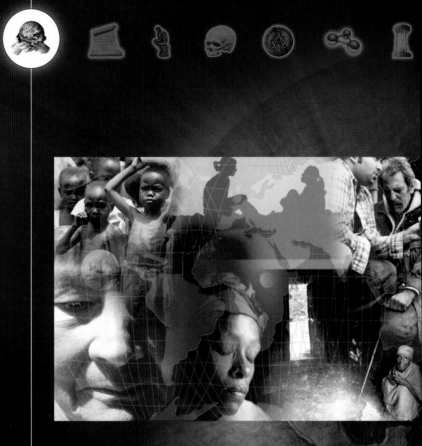

Community & Involvement:
God Cares; Do I?

Introduction

For many centuries, Christians have taken it upon themselves to address the needs of the poor and the outcast in their own communities. But today, much of that work is left to the state. Even the general call for involvement in our culture at large has become a matter of debate in some contemporary Christian circles.

A careful examination of Scripture will reveal that believers have a mandate to reclaim their place in this important arena. We dare not, like Jonah, try to escape God's call to be involved.

TheTruthProject

Quote Unquote

What does Scripture say? Fill in the blanks as you watch this presentation.

1. "Which of these three do you think was a neighbor to the man who fell into the hands of robbers?" The expert in the law replied, "The one who _____ _____ ____ _____." —*Luke 10:36-37*

2. He raises the _____ from the dust and lifts the _____ from the ash heap; he seats them with princes and has them inherit a throne of honor. —*1 Samuel 2:8*

3. "Take my yoke upon you and learn from me, for I am _____ and _____ ____ _____, and you will find rest for your souls." —*Matthew 11:28-29*

4. For God did not give us a spirit of _____, but a spirit of power, of love and of self-discipline. —*2 Timothy 1:7*

5. My whole being will exclaim, "Who is like you, O LORD? You _____ the poor from those too strong for them, the poor and needy from those who rob them." —*Psalm 35:10*

6. But Nineveh has more than a hundred and twenty thousand people who cannot tell their _____ _____ from their _____, and many cattle as well. —*Jonah 4:9-11*

Notes or Questions

While watching the video, use these lines to record your thoughts, any facts you want to remember, questions that arise, etc.

_____

_____

_____

_____

_____

_____

_____

_____

_____

_____

_____

_____

_____

_____

_____

_____

_____

_____

_____

_____

_____

_____

_____

"You are the salt of the earth. But if the salt loses its saltiness, how can it be made salty again?"

Matthew 5:13

Truth 1 | God So Loves the World

Our Lord is actively involved in this world, and He wants us to join Him in that work.

1. Does God care just about saving individuals, or does He want to renew the whole cosmos? Has He given up on the physical universe He once made? Consider the words of Genesis 1; Romans 8:18-25; Colossians 1:15-20.

_____

_____

_____

2. Dr. Tackett runs through a long list of all the things he sees God doing in the world. Have fun creating your own list (maybe on an extra sheet of blank paper!).

_____

_____

_____

Truth 2 | Who Is My Neighbor?

*We are called especially to reach out to our "neighbor" in need—
including the poor, the orphans, widows, and outcasts.*

1. Who are *our* neighbors? Who is poor in some way? Who are the
lonely and outcast, and what are we being called to do for each of those
individuals? What did C.S. Lewis mean when he said that "there are no
ordinary people. You have never talked to a mere mortal"?

_____

_____

_____

_____

_____

2. What is it in God's nature that makes Him care especially for widows
and orphans and outcasts? Do we really care for the needy? Whom do we
weep and pray for often? What tangible help do we offer?

_____

_____

_____

_____

3. How do you feel about the fact that God, the Lord of Creation, is
humble and gentle? Do *you* find it difficult to be humble? To do away with
pride? What is the difference between humility and timidity?

_____

_____

_____

_____

Truth 3 | Pulling a Jonah

Today's Christians are relatively uninvolved in the culture, compared to believers who've gone before.

1. What examples from the past or present make you feel good about the Christian community's involvement in the world?

_____

_____

_____

_____

2. Why are some Christians today seemingly reluctant to help out a "sinking ship"? Where do you think we got the idea that God is interested only in saving us and getting us to heaven, rather than resurrecting our bodies for eternal life in a new earth?

_____

_____

_____

_____

3. For you, what is a good balance between church activities (mingling with other Christians) and community involvement? Is one keeping you from doing the other?

_____

_____

_____

_____

Wrap-Up

The Bible clearly presents the perplexing reality that God has entrusted us with carrying out His mission and purpose in the world.

The God of the Scriptures is the lord of the lonely, the savior of the outcast, the defender of the defenseless, and the sustainer of all who find themselves in need. Our call is to become like Him by discovering what it means to love not only Him, but also our neighbor.

Check It Out

For your reference and further review, here are some of the key Scripture passages that were mentioned in the video you just watched.

Deuteronomy 6:4-9;
15:11; 24:14

1 Samuel 2:1-10

Job 5:11,15

Psalm 12:5; 22:4;
35:10; 138:6

Proverbs 14:21; 28:27

Isaiah 57:15; 65:1-2

Jonah 4:9-11

Matthew 5:43-44;
11:28-29; 19:16-17;
22:33-40; 23:37-38;
25:33-36

Luke 1:51-52; 10:25-37

John 13; 14:4-9; 17:6

2 Timothy 1:7; 2:15

James 2:8; 4:6

1 Peter 5:5-6

1 John 3:17

For more study aids
and other resources, visit
the small-group support site at
mytruthproject.org

Answers

Lesson 1

Quote Unquote

1. truth
2. lie
3. captives
4. What is truth
5. reality
6. lie
7. bamboo tree
8. really real
9. who God is
10. character, nature, being

What Is What?

1. e
2. j
3. a
4. g
5. b
6. f
7. h
8. d
9. i
10. c

Lesson 2

Quote Unquote

1. captive
2. cosmos
3. assumptive language
4. ultimate reality
5. universals, particulars
6. dead
7. ought
8. nine
9. life system
10. transformed

What Is What?

1. b
2. i
3. d
4. j
5. c
6. a
7. h
8. e
9. f
10. g

Lesson 3

Quote Unquote

1. ourselves
2. Spirit, Spirit
3. human nature
4. boy
5. live for himself
6. pollywog
7. straw, straw, straw
8. evil
9. foreign
10. cultural influences

What Is What?

1. e
2. c
3. f
4. d
5. a
6. g
7. i
8. b
9. h

Lesson 4

Quote Unquote

1. theologians
2. shadow over His face
3. intimate, intimate, intimate
4. Father
5. Jealous, jealous
6. ourselves
7. trustworthiness of the Scripture
8. destroy
9. 82

What Is What?

1. g
2. i
3. e
4. c
5. a
6. f
7. h
8. d
9. b

Lesson 5

Quote Unquote

1. eternal power, divine nature
2. time
3. rational order, harmony
4. fact
5. appearance
6. peacock's tail
7. fossil record
8. machines
9. Jesus' earthly life

What Is What?

1. d
2. f
3. a
4. j
5. b
6. e
7. h
8. c
9. i
10. g

Lesson 6

Quote Unquote

1. advancement, Christian faith
2. past, present
3. controls, controls
4. forget, remember, remember, forget
5. modern world
6. identity, wisdom
7. forget
8. plans, purposes
9. metanarratives

What Is What?

1. b
2. a
3. j
4. g
5. d
6. c
7. i
8. e
9. f
10. h

Lesson 7

Quote Unquote

1. unity, diversity
2. substance
3. social order
4. triune
5. divine imprint
6. head, head
7. shepherds

What Is What?

1. e
2. g
3. b
4. a
5. c
6. f
7. d
8. h

Lesson 8

Quote Unquote

1. live
2. remains
3. Counselor
4. dwelling
5. glory
6. one, one, one, one, one, one
7. Love one another, love one another, love one another
8. in secret, in secret
9. pants

Lesson 9

Quote Unquote

1. terrible monster
2. atrocities
3. violence
4. governments
5. manipulation
6. cultural influences
7. objective
8. family
9. national sovereignty

Lesson 10

Quote Unquote

1. unproved, outmoded
2. Cross of Christ
3. Christian Religion
4. religion, morality
5. happiness
6. liberty
7. freedom
8. Constitution
9. civilization

What Is What?

1. c
2. e
3. b
4. a
5. j
6. d
7. f
8. h
9. i
10. g

Lesson 11

Quote Unquote

1. sabbath
2. painful
3. cattle
4. subdue
5. Lord, Lord
6. poverty
7. Money
8. love of God

Lesson 12

Quote Unquote

1. had mercy on him
2. poor, needy
3. gentle, humble in heart
4. timidity
5. rescue
6. right hand, left

More **Worldview** Resources

TrueU™
Experience a fusion
of fact & faith with
the *TrueU* DVD series!

The creators of *Focus on the Family's The Truth Project®*
have produced a worldview program designed especiall
for teens and college students. In three powerful DVD
sets, *TrueU* answers the critical questions students ask:
Does God Exist?, *Is the Bible Reliable?* and *Who is Jesus
Really?* *TrueU* will equip you to defend your faith and
become a world-changer in an increasingly hostile culture

Focus on the Family's
The Truth Project® Study Guide
Buy in bulk and save!

The Truth Project Study Guide is an outstanding
supplement to *The Truth Project* and a must for
every member of your small group. *The Study Guide*
complements *The Truth Project Leader's Guide* featured
in *Focus on the Family's The Truth Project* DVD set. It is
an invaluable resource for every participant, providing
additional insights, a place for notetaking and an
ongoing personal reference. Can be purchased alone
or in packages of five.

Focus on the Family's
The Truth Project®
Daily Travelogue
Enhance your small-group experience!

Written specifically for *The Truth Project* participants,
The Truth Project Daily Travelogue provides scripturally
anchored reflections and prayers for each of the 91 days
in the 13-week small group experience. *The Travelogue*
enables readers to grapple with key concepts on a
deeper, more experiential level, preparing them for a life-
changing, personal encounter with the Author of all truth.

To order visit: FocusOnTheFamily ... /T ... P